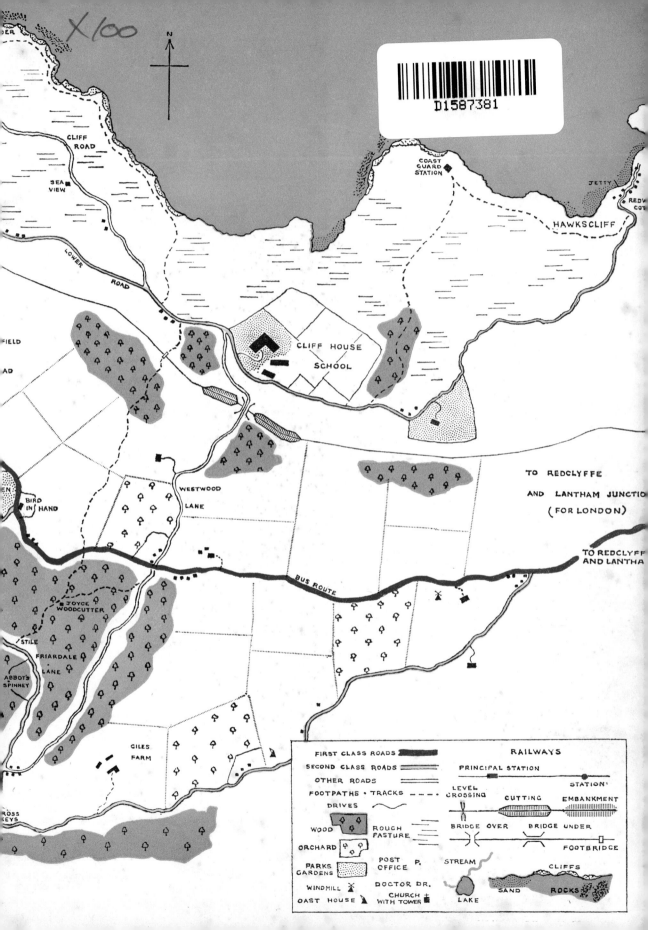

Greyfriars School
A Prospectus

Greyfriars School
A Prospectus

by

J. S. Butcher Esq.

TOGETHER WITH SOME NOTES AND COMMENTS
ON THE TEACHING STAFF, SCHOLARS AND
DOMESTIC STAFF, AND ON THE ENVIRONS,
HISTORY AND SPORTING ACHIEVEMENTS
OF THE SCHOOL, COMPILED FROM THE
RECORDS OF THE LATE

FRANK RICHARDS, ESQ.

---

and published by
CASSELL · LONDON

CASSELL & COMPANY LTD
35 RED LION SQUARE, LONDON WCI
MELBOURNE, SYDNEY, TORONTO
JOHANNESBURG, CAPE TOWN, AUCKLAND

Printed in Great Britain by
Butler & Tanner Ltd, Frome and London

Conamur tenues Grandia

Greyfriars School
Friardale—Kent

FOUNDED 1551

Headmaster: The Rev. H. H. Locke, D.D.
Telephone: Courtfield 106

THE ARMORIAL BEARINGS OF GREYFRIARS SCHOOL

*Azure two keys in pale the wards outwards Gold enclosing in chief a book
leathered Argent edged with its clasp open to the dexter also Gold ensigning
an apple tree proper its trunk and the fruit thereof Gold: And for the
Crest, upon a Helm Mantling Azure doubled Argent and Gold with
a wreath Argent Gold and Azure a friar's bust proper hooded of grey
all within an arch of English perpendicular style also Gold,
and for the Motto:* CONAMUR TENUES GRANDIA.

THE MOTTO

CONAMUR TENUES GRANDIA

Horace: *Odes* I, vi, 9. *Though slight we strive for greatness*

The Armorial Bearings of Greyfriars School cannot be established with any certainty from the published records. Consultations have taken place at the College of Arms with a view to establishing whether or not the Armorial Bearings that it seems evident were appropriate for the School were documented in any way at the College, but the Arms and Crest depicted by them are more in the nature of a reconstruction than what can be regarded as an official record of the College.

Greyfriars School

CHAIRMAN OF THE BOARD OF GOVERNORS
Sir Hilton Popper

HEADMASTER
The Rev. Herbert Henry Locke, D.D.

FORM MASTERS*
Sixth—*The Headmaster*
Fifth—*Paul Pontifex Prout, Esq., M.A.*
The Shell—*Horace Manfred Hacker, Esq., B.A.*
Upper Fourth—*Algernon Jasper Capper, Esq., M.A.*
Lower Fourth (The Remove)—*Horace Henry Samuel Quelch,
Esq., M.A.*
Third—*Herbert Wiggins, Esq., M.A.*
Second—*Eusebius Twigg, Esq., B.A., B.Sc.*
First—*Bernard Morrison Twigg, Esq., B.A.*†

ASSISTANT MASTERS
Mathematics and Games—*Lawrence Lascelles, Esq.*
French—*M. Henri Charpentier*
German—*Herr Otto Gans*

LIBRARIAN
Mr Woose

---

* The number of forms was originally seven, a First form being established later. The exact date of this addition has not been positively traced in the existing records, but it was probably during the year 1923. The First Form boys are known as "The Babes", and have little contact with other Scholars.

† An earlier First Form master was Mr Walter Bunter, a cousin of a present Scholar of the School. Following Mr Bunter's departure for another post, some reorganisation of the teaching staff took place, involving the Third, Second and First forms.

The School

Greyfriars School is located in unspoilt country surroundings, within easy reach of the coast of Kent and in close proximity to the River Sark. Near by is pretty Friardale village with, at a short distance, the interesting and historic town of Courtfield.

Being of ancient foundation, the School buildings have weathered picturesquely with time. During periods of renovation, their appearance has been carefully preserved by successive Governing Boards.

Certain interior modernisation has been introduced from time to time, for the added comfort and well-being of the Scholars, but the School authorities have taken great care to retain all the features and mementoes of bygone days.

The School environs comprise pleasant wooded grounds, of which the ruins of the old monastic foundation form a fascinating part. Extensive playing fields provide ample space for all the recognised School games.

As the visitor approaches Greyfriars, its mellowed façade and ivy-covered tower—dominating a rural setting—present an attractive picture of this famous Public School.

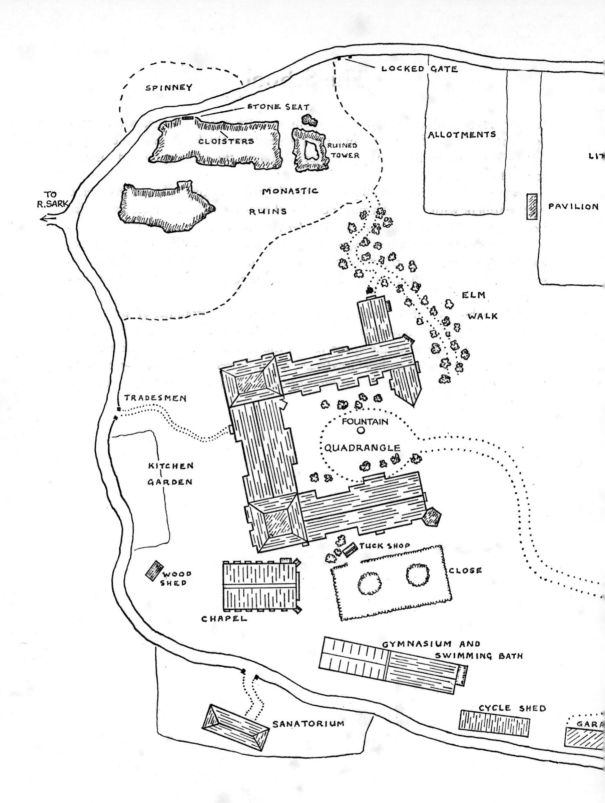

Greyfriars School

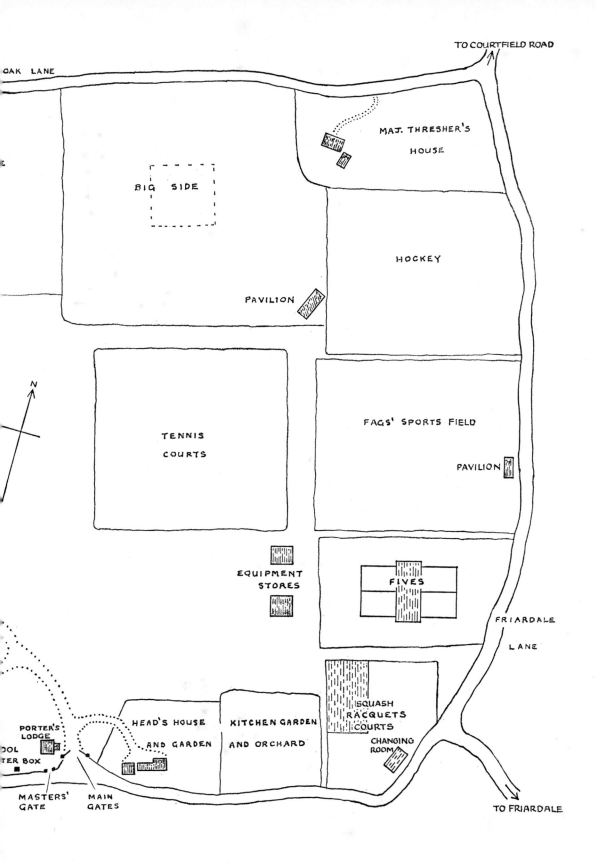

A Short History of the School

The origins of the monastic buildings, according to Mr Quelch's *A History of Greyfriars*, can be traced back to

> the days of Anfrith, the so-called "Black" Monk. He was a strange character. Beginning his career as a soldier, he afterwards became a hermit in the Romney Marshes. Years later Anfrith became a genuine monk of the Augustinian or Austin Friars order and to him, it seems, we owe the foundation stones of the original building, later enlarged by the Grey Friars.

The Ancient Order of the Grey Friars founded the Monastery in the year 1472.

During King Henry VIII's campaign for the "Dissolution of the Monasteries" the great building was closed. In their endeavour to escape the King's attention, the Friars hid in the Crypt and later continued for a time to exist in the vaults beneath the Priory and the Chapel. An unknown traitor, however, for a reward offered by the King, betrayed the Friars who, on appearing before Henry, were offered their freedom on condition that they revealed the whereabouts of the reputed gold treasure and valuable ornaments of the Monastery. The Friars, defying the King, remained steadfast in face of his threats and eventually paid the penalty of execution. The King had many searches made of the buildings, without success; to this day the legendary treasure has remained undiscovered.

There followed a period of neglect and decay until, to quote again from Mr Quelch's invaluable history, in 1551 Edward VI restored and opened the buildings

> as a school for poor, but studious boys, whose parents could not afford to have them educated. This prospered slowly until the reign of Charles II, when a newly erected wing and two-thirds of the original building were burnt to the ground.

Some fifty years later a new college was built for gentlemen's sons and in 1716 Greyfriars, in its present form, was set on the career which has led to its present prominence among the great Public Schools.

The remains of the original building are now in ruins:

> There is the wonderful Old Priory, with its vaults and subterranean tunnel leading to the Crypt beneath the ruined Chapel in the Cloisters. East of the Cloisters there is the curious, old, ivy-covered tower, surrounded by a mass of fallen pillars of masonry. This, and the shady grass-covered land around, is all that is left of the famous old Monastery of the first Grey Friars.

From time to time, discovery of hidden rooms and passages has been recorded. A secret tunnel was found leading from Friardale Wood to the

School, and mention is made that "in the more ancient parts of Greyfriars* secret passages were known to exist, dating from the old monastic days".

In common with other ancient establishments, and apart from the incidents recorded above, Greyfriars has shared in moments of history.

In 1564 Queen Elizabeth I visited the School. The Headmaster had the honour of entertaining Her Majesty and "Good Queen Bess" was acclaimed with great enthusiasm by the Scholars.

In 1643, at about the time of the Battle of Newbury, the School was involved in a minor clash with Parliamentarian troops—the sympathies of the Head and the Scholars were mainly with King Charles I. Although, as is generally known, the Parliamentarians later occupied such establishments, Greyfriars apparently escaped this indignity. Possibly the local Cromwellian commander decided that the Scholars, however Royalist, would not create much trouble for the Roundhead cause, or perhaps he had more pressing problems elsewhere in the district.

That as far as we can discover, is the last appearance of Greyfriars School in the great main stream of England's history. Thereafter, the School withdrew from public view, developing steadily but quietly as monarch succeeded monarch upon the Nation's throne. The School was content simply to play its part in the order of things, performing its duties and fulfilling its responsibilities according to the pattern laid down by its founders, ever responsive to change and improvement, yet standing firmly on its tried and tested traditions of service and scholarship.

By the early years of this century, Greyfriars had become to all intents and purposes the School we know today. In the first "Great War", to which many Greyfriars Scholars went so bravely, a number of German bombs fell near the School itself, but apart from the shaking, the old and well-loved buildings remained unharmed.

In the Second World War, Greyfriars Scholars again played their full part in every theatre of operations. Although the School lay in the county over which so much of the Battle of Britain was fought, and in the paths of V.1 "doodlebugs" and V.2 rockets on their way from their launching sites to London, the School was again unharmed.

After the war, Greyfriars School took on a new lease of life, as the many published records prove. Now, over four hundred years after its foundation by the pious young King, it is a national institution. Well might we gaze at its mellowed buildings and to the old poet's

CONAMUR TENUES GRANDIA

reply "Aye, and that right mightily."

---

* Presumably referring to what are now the ruins.

School Organisation and Miscellaneous Information

Curriculum

A comprehensive general education is provided in the following main subjects: English, Mathematics, Geography, History, Latin, French, German, Science (Physics, Chemistry, Biology and Zoology); Art and Music are optional.

Certain class periods are allocated to craft training in the School workshops, but these courses also become optional at a later stage of the Scholar's training.

Scholars are coached to take Ordinary levels of the General Certificate of Education, and subsequently are prepared for Advanced levels, for Universities and the professions.

Schools

From the Sixth to Shell forms inclusive, Scholars are considered to be "Upper School" or "Seniors"; from the Upper Fourth downwards, boys are known as "Lower School" or "Juniors".

For games, however, the grouping is somewhat different. Division is made into Seniors, Middle School and Juniors.

School Terms and Holidays

The School year consists of three terms: Michaelmas, Easter and Summer.

In common with other Public Schools, holidays are usually four weeks at Christmas, four at Easter and eight weeks in the Summer.

Speech Day

An annual event of great importance, when the Governing Board is in attendance and parents and guardians are invited to the School. It is the occasion for the presentation of prizes and awards to boys for academic achievement and prowess in sports and games.

Open Days

Parents and guardians are welcome to visit the School on the occasions of Speech Day, Founder's Day and the Annual Sports Day. At other times, the Headmaster expects to have prior advice of an intended visit.

Guests

When necessary, several guest rooms are available to visitors. It is requested, however, that whenever possible, prior notice be given of requirements.

School Timetable*

Rising Bell	SUMMER 6.30 a.m.	WINTER 7.30 a.m.
Chapel	SUMMER 7.15 a.m.	WINTER 8.00 a.m.
Breakfast	SUMMER 7.45 a.m.	WINTER 8.30 a.m.
Morning School	9.00 a.m.–12.00	
Morning Break*	10.45 a.m.–11.00 a.m.	
Dinner	1.00 p.m.	
Afternoon School (EXCEPT WEDNESDAY AND SATURDAY)	2.00 p.m.–4.00 p.m.	
Recreation	4.00 p.m.–7.00 p.m.	
Tea In Hall	5.30 p.m.	
Call Over*	7.00 p.m.	
Preparation* (EXCEPT SUNDAY)	7.30 p.m.–8.30 p.m.	
Supper	8.45 p.m.	
Dormitory Bell*	JUNIORS 9.00 p.m.	SENIORS 9.45 p.m.
Lights Out	JUNIORS 9.15 p.m.	SENIORS 10.00 p.m.

Meals

All meals are normally taken in the Dining Hall, with the exception that for the Sixth to Lower Fourth forms, tea in Hall is optional and, if desired, Scholars in these forms may provide their own tea in studies.

Tea in Studies (from the Sixth to the Lower Fourth only)
Tea may be taken between 4.30 p.m. and 6.30 p.m.

Half-day Holidays:
On Wednesday and Saturday, from 12 noon. Games are always organised for these afternoons. Additional holidays are granted on special occasions such as Speech Day and Founder's Day.

Sunday
Services are held in the School Chapel morning and evening. Arrangements for worship can be made for Scholars of denominations other than Church of England. On this day boys are expected to wear their best clothes and to occupy themselves with local walks, study and reading, or other quiet pursuits.

Lights Out
Is checked at 10.30 p.m. by masters and prefects.

Passes
Late passes out of gates are granted at the discretion of masters and prefects. Passes out of bounds are considered on application to form-masters only.

---

* From a study of the School records, it would appear that this timetable is subject to amendment from time to time, at the Headmaster's and sometimes the form-masters' discretion.

Reports

End of term reports are sent to the boys' parents or guardians.

Competitions and Prizes

Several open contests are held annually on a variety of subjects, offering prizes of cash or books, and Scholars are encouraged to participate.

Two of the most important are the Founder's Prize (current value £20) and the Governors' Examination (current value £50).

Preparation

Scholars of forms from the Sixth down to Lower Fourth are allowed to take preparation in studies. All other forms take preparation in class rooms, supervised by a master or prefect.

Detention

Detention periods are held regularly under the supervision of M. Charpentier.

School Dress

The regulation dress is—School blazer, grey trousers, School cap and School tie of blue and white diagonal stripes. Certain variations in trouser patterns are allowed, but the selection is limited and all articles must be obtained from the official suppliers.*

Medical Care

The School has a well-equipped Sanatorium at a short distance from the main building. Minor ailments are dealt with by the School Matron; a local doctor is appointed Medical Officer to the School and he visits whenever necessary.

Bathrooms, etc.

Ample bath and toilet facilities are provided for the Scholars, on all three floors of the main building.

Laundry

There are up-to-date installations for dealing with Scholars' personal laundry on the School premises.

---

* Earlier School dress was "Eton" jackets for Juniors and "Tails" for Seniors. No positive date of changeover has been found, but it apparently occurred in the early 1930s. Similarly, boaters seem to have gone out of fashion in recent years. There is a variation in blazers, caps and ties for "Colours" awarded in games. (*See also* School Games and Sports.)

Prefects

The prefectorial system has long been established at Greyfriars. Appointments are made by the Headmaster from the Sixth form only. The position is considered to be a great honour by the Scholars. Not only do prefects materially assist masters in maintaining discipline, but the appointment provides them with valuable experience in practical leadership and administration.*

Prefects are allowed to cane boys as punishment for minor offences.

Studies

All Scholars, from the Fifth to Lower Fourth inclusive, have private, furnished rooms, which, in many cases, are shared by two or more persons. The Sixth form enjoy individual rooms, which are not numbered but have the occupants' names displayed on the doors. The boys may introduce additional items of furnishing, subject to their form-master's approval.

Study occupants are allowed to have fires in their rooms and all concerned favour the retention of solid fuel, rather than having central heating installed.†

Common Rooms

Adequate common or recreation rooms are provided for the boys.

Over the years, custom has created certain popular gathering places for different forms; e.g., the Fifth prefer their Games Study; the Remove invariably congregate in the Rag; the Third and Second forms have a habit of gathering in their class rooms for recreation. These traditional preferences are now semi-officially recognised by the authorities.

Fags

"Fagging" for Sixth Formers has been a custom at Greyfriars for many years. It is confined to boys in the Third and Second (hence the general term "fags" applied to juniors of these forms).

Their duties consist generally of tidying studies, preparing tea, running errands and a certain amount of cleaning—shoes, sports gear, etc.

At the call of "Fag", the nearest boy within hearing is expected to report to the caller.‡

---

* School records indicate that prefectorial strength has varied between seven and nine. The current roll is: Wingate (Head Prefect), Carne, Faulkner, Gwynne, Hammersley, Loder, North, Tremaine, Walker.

† Several alterations in the Remove study passage have been recorded. Originally there were twelve studies; No. 13 was added when Cherry moved from No. 1, and No. 14 was converted from a box-room when Bull and Fish arrived. At one time, Bunter shared No. 1 room with Wharton and Nugent, and at another, much appreciated period, had a room to himself. *See* page 46.

‡ No mention has been found in School records as to whether all Sixth Formers are entitled to this benefit, but various accounts of School happenings suggest that only prefects excercise the privilege.

First Night of Term

Another event in the Greyfriars calendar when tradition reigns. It is customary for singing to take place in Hall—a lusty performance, enjoyed by all. A popular School song for these occasions is "The Jolly Old Friar", the words of which, set to music by Mr Malcolm Arnold, can be found on pages 18–19.*

Old Boys Association

This is a lively and well-supported organisation, which has an important say in all decisions made by the Board of Governors regarding the progress and welfare of Greyfriars and its Scholars.

It is understood that there is a proposal afoot to modify the title to "Old Greys", a suggestion which is being favourably considered.

There are two annual reunions, on Midsummer Day and New Year's Eve, at a time and place announced by the Committee. Additional gatherings are held when the occasion warrants.

The Old Boys annually meet to play football and cricket against the School Senior XIs.

Many of the exhibits and books in the School Museum and Libraries have been presented by members of the Old Boys Association.

Clubs and Societies

Throughout the School all Scholars are encouraged to become members of School clubs and societies, which embrace a wide field of interests and activities. Although under the general supervision of masters, they are principally organised and conducted by the Scholars themselves, who thus have an opportunity to gain valuable experience of administration. Various form and School societies have been established, including Amateur Dramatics (a well-equipped modern stage is maintained in Big Hall), Debating, Chess, Photography, etc.†

School Magazine

Entitled *The Greyfriars Herald*, this is edited and published by the Lower Fourth. It mirrors everyday life and views of the School, its Staff and Scholars. The bulk of the material is submitted by the Scholars themselves, but contributions are welcomed from all sources.

One very popular feature of the *Herald* is the amusing adventures of the

---

* An earlier setting for "The Jolly Old Friar" was composed by Mr Jeff Lytton.
† Current officials in the Lower Fourth:

Dramatic Society: PRESIDENT—Wharton
　　　　　　　　　GENERAL MANAGER—Wibley
Debating Society: PRESIDENT—Wharton

boys of "St Sam's" and their eccentric Headmaster, "Dr Birchemall"—written by Nugent of the Second Form.*

Library
The School Library has an excellent reference and non-fiction section and a comprehensive collection of fiction, together with a widely representative subscription to contemporary newspapers and magazines, local and national, all under the care of the School Librarian, Mr Woose.

Museums
The School has interesting Art and Natural History Museums. These have long been the special concern of the Old Boys' Association which, through successive generations, has made valuable contributions to both Library and Museums.

Mail
Incoming mail is placed in racks in the main entrance-hall and can be collected by the Scholars during morning break. A post box is provided in the main entrance-hall, and a letter-box is by the main gates.

Notice Boards
These can be found in the entrance-halls and are for the display of official notices, team selections, sports fixtures, club and society announcements, etc.

School Shop
The Tuck Shop, established during the reign of Queen Anne, and now managed by Mrs Jessie Mimble, is a picturesque building standing beneath the elms in a corner of the Close.

A comprehensive stock of confectionery, light refreshments and sundries, is maintained. The Shop is open at specified times during the day, at

---

* Present Editorial Staff of *The Greyfriars Herald*:

EDITOR—Wharton
SUB-EDITORS—Cherry; Nugent Major
SPORTS EDITOR—Vernon-Smith
SOCIAL AND FASHIONS EDITOR—Lord Mauleverer

From a random inspection of issues of the *Herald*, interesting tit-bits of information come to light. For instance, we learn from one report that unofficial combats to settle disputes or matters of "honour" usually take place behind the Chapel. Again, from an interview we learn that the first of the "Famous Five" to arrive at Greyfriars was Nugent Major, followed by Wharton; Cherry came next, then Hurree Singh and lastly Bull. Before Johnny Bull arrived the company was known as the "Famous Four".

weekends, and on half-days and half-holidays. There is a School song about the Tuck Shop, which has as one verse:

> *Long live the Tuck Shop! Place of cheer*
> *Which gains our warm approval;*
> *Thank goodness we need never fear*
> *Its permanent removal.*
> *So long as Greyfriars stands erect,*
> *And keeps its proud position,*
> *The famous Tuck Shop, we expect,*
> *Will carry on its mission.*

The Jolly Old Friar
A Greyfriars School Song

Music by
Mr MALCOLM ARNOLD

Words by
Mr FRANK RICHARDS

CHORUS

Good old Grey friars, sec-ond to none, past and pre-sent, and

for-ty years on; nev-er in the cart, ev-er in the van, for

that is the way of a Grey — friars man.

"THE JOLLY OLD FRIAR"

'Twas a jolly old friar of orders grey,
Who founded a school when he came this way;
And since that far date, umpteen years ago,
Good old Greyfriars School has continued to grow.
There may be a school somewhere that is our match,
But we hardly believe that there can be;
We rather think Greyfriars the best of the batch,
At the top, at the top, right up at the top of the tree.

Chorus: Good Old Greyfriars, second to none
Past and present, and forty years on;
Never in the cart, ever in the van,
For that is the way of a Greyfriars man.

Chorus repeated ad lib.

School Games and Sports

The principal School games are Association Football and cricket. Facilities and grounds are also available for hockey, fives, squash rackets, tennis and swimming. Other activities include boxing, athletics (field, track and cross-country) and rowing. The School has a fine outdoor swimming pool and a well-equipped gymnasium.

Overall supervision of Games is exercised by Mr Lawrence Lascelles (Games Master); direct administration is the responsibility of the Head of Games (George Wingate).

On Wednesday afternoons, "Games" are compulsory, and every boy has to participate, unless excused on medical grounds.

Each form, from the Sixth to the Lower Fourth inclusive, has its own football and cricket XIs. The Second and Third forms usually combine forces to field XIs for these games.

The School is represented by Senior, Middle School and Junior teams in all sports and games. Regular fixtures are arranged with other schools, including St Jim's, Rookwood, Highcliffe, Courtfield Grammar and Redclyffe.

"Colours"—represented variously by distinctive blazers, caps, hatbands, ties, etc.—are awarded to outstanding members of School teams by team captains, with the agreement of the Head of Games and Games Master.

A silver cup, presented by the Board of Governors, is awarded annually to the best all-round athlete in each form.

Sports Day

An important annual event in the Greyfriars calendar is Sports Day, when the finals of all athletic events are held. It is a tradition that every boy, unless medically unfit, enters for at least one of the many events that are staged with the finals, and the masters enter into the spirit of Sports Day by holding their own Masters' Race.

Sports Notes and Records

Football

Greyfriars School has won the Public Schools' Challenge Cup on five occasions. The most famous occasion was in the season 1895–6, when the final—against Greyfriars' old rivals, St Jim's—was played no less than five times. The first four contests were drawn, and only in the fifth did Greyfriars gain the victory.

The Greyfriars Senior XI had its most successful season 1907–8; with the exception of one drawn game, every match was won.

Record attendance at a Greyfriars match is 4,270 in 1904, when the School played Highcliffe in the Third Round of the Public Schools' Challenge Cup.

The Senior XI record win is 14—0 against Friardale Athletic.*

Cricket

Greyfriars played its first recorded cricket match in 1822, against a famous Canterbury school, and won by five runs. Several Greyfriars Old Boys have played for their County sides.

A long-standing record score by a Greyfriars Senior XI was 640 for 5 (declared) against Friardale Village, in 1899. This was, however, recently beaten by a score of 672 against the same club. During this game Patrick Gwynne scored 226 not out.†

Record individual score for the Senior XI is that by H. V. Clifton—244 against Friardale Village in 1899. In 1897 the same player scored a century in each of seven consecutive matches.

The School's finest bowling feat is that by E. W. Dartforth in 1911. Playing for the Senior XI against Courtfield Wanderers, he took all ten wickets for only two runs.

Champion stonewaller of Greyfriars was J. B. Sturgess, who once scored only eight runs in just over two hours.

School cricket pavilions on Big Side have been twice destroyed by fire—in 1875 and 1900. The present buildings are well equipped with fire extinguishers.

Boxing—in the Gymnasium and elsewhere. Some famous fights

In 1875, Tom Power, then Captain of the School, fought Fowkes of the Fifth form, a notorious bully; Power won after fifteen of the most exciting rounds ever seen at the School.

In the same year two Sixth Formers, Jack Pryor and Stanley Ransom, decided to settle a long-standing feud by fighting it out. The contest was arranged to take place in a secluded clearing of Friardale Wood. The fight continued for many rounds—the men being evenly matched. Eventually

---

* Record victory for a Remove XI is 17—1 against Wapshot Juniors, when Wharton scored eight times. In fairness it must be mentioned that Wapshot had two men injured for most of the game.

† The highest score by a Remove XI is 720, against Courtfield Juniors in 1850. Record individual score by a present-day Remove Scholar is the 226 not out by Wharton, against Bunter's XI.

In one innings in 1910, Remove wicket-keeper Norman Howard took eight catches behind the stumps.

Pryor was knocked out, but almost at the same second Ransom went to the ground. The sequel was a happy one; both fellows were leaving the School at the end of that term and they departed the best of friends.

In 1899 Harcourt and Hawkes, both of the Sixth, met to decide who was unofficial champion of the School. There followed a long, gruelling tussle, which was stopped by the arrival of the Head. The fight was, however, continued later in Friardale Wood, and finally Harcourt triumphed. According to verbal records, the contest lasted for something over fourteen rounds.

The quickest fight recorded is that between Victor Yorke of Greyfriars and Harry Hodges from Courtfield, in 1905. Yorke had delivered a knock-out in five seconds.

Recent Sports News

Cricket

The Senior XI won 15 matches out of 20, lost 1 and drew 4. There appear to have been few outstanding batting performances in the Senior XI, but as a bowler Tom North clean bowled six men for no runs in one match.

Hurree Singh had best Junior XI bowling figures, taking 100 wickets for an average of six runs each.

The Remove XI won 14 out of 22 matches. Wharton led the Remove batting list with an average of 44. He scored four centuries, including 120 not out against Rookwood.

Football

A match between the Old Boys and the Senior XI was a great struggle, the Seniors winning 3—2, all three goals scored by Wingate.

The Senior XI beat Courtfield Athletic 10—0.

The Remove XI beat Friardale Village 10—0, Frank Nugent scoring five goals.

A Typical Remove Football XI

G. Bulstrode

J. Bull   S. Q. I. Field

R. Penfold   M. Linley   P. Todd

H. Vernon-Smith   R. Cherry   H. Wharton   H. Singh   F. Nugent

23

A Year's Remove Champions

	Champion	Runner-up
Best all-round footballer[1]	H. Vernon-Smith	H. Wharton
Best all-round cricketer[1]	H. Wharton	H. Singh
Tennis	T. Redwing	H. Singh
Athletics:		
100 yards	H. Vernon-Smith	F. Nugent
Quarter-mile	P. Todd	R. Cherry
Mile	H. Wharton	H. Vernon-Smith
Marathon*	M. Linley	H. Wharton
High jump	F. Nugent	R. Rake
Long jump	R. Cherry	T. Brown
Throwing cricket ball	J. Bull	G. Bulstrode
Boxing	R. Cherry	R. Russell
Wrestling	P. Todd	D. Morgan
Swimming	M. Linley	H. Wharton
Diving	F. Nugent	P. Todd
Water Polo[1]	R. Cherry	M. Desmond
Sculling	J. Bull	T. Redwing
Cycling	T. Brown	S. Q. I. Field
Rifle Shooting	P. Todd	S. Q. I. Field
Gymnastics	O. Kipps	Wun Lung
Chess	H. Singh	P. Todd
Table Tennis	Wun Lung	W. Wibley
Table Football	R. Cherry	R. Penfold
Race to Tuck Shop	W. G. Bunter	The rest—nowhere

[1] Decided by Form ballot

Remove Boxers in order of merit (decided on points)

1 R. Cherry	11 G. Bulstrode
2 R. Russell and H. Wharton	12 F. Nugent
4 M. Linley and P. Todd	13 R. Penfold
6 T. Redwing	14 P. Delarey
7 J. Bull	15 M. Newland
8 H. Vernon-Smith	16 P. Bolsover
9 S. Q. I. Field	17 H. Singh
10 T. Brown	18 D. Ogilvy

* The School "Marathons" are not of course run over the Olympic distance, but are really cross-country races to which the name Marathon was given—and has stuck.

24

19 R. Rake

20 M. Desmond

21 R. Hillary

22 H. P. Mauleverer

23 D. Morgan and T. Dutton

25 O. Kipps and W. Wilbey

27 S. Snoop

28 P. Hazeldene and J. Vivian

30 R. Smith

31 A. Treluce

32 H. Skinner

33 H. Trevor and F. Fish

35 W. Stott and N. Dupont

37 Wun Lung and W. G. Bunter

Greyfriars School

FLOOR PLANS

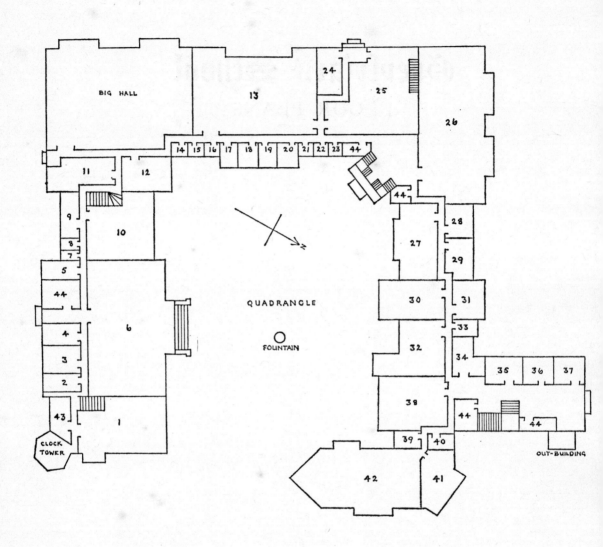

Greyfriars School
GROUND FLOOR PLAN

1 NATURAL HISTORY MUSEUM

2 HEADMASTER'S STUDY

3 GOVERNORS' ROOM

4 RECEPTION ROOM

5 BURSAR'S ROOM

6 ENTRANCE AND ASSEMBLY HALL

7 SECRETARY'S OFFICE

8 MATRON'S OFFICE

9 SENIOR ART STUDIO

10 SENIOR COMMON ROOM

11 PREFECTS' ROOM

12 MASTERS' DINING ROOM

13 DINING HALL

14 MR E. TWIGG'S STUDY

15 MR WIGGINS'S STUDY

16 MR B. M. TWIGG'S STUDY

17 MR CAPPER'S STUDY

18 MR PROUT'S STUDY

19 MR HACKER'S STUDY

20 MR QUELCH'S STUDY

21 MR LASCELLES'S STUDY

22 M. CHARPENTIER'S STUDY

23 HERR OTTO GANS'S STUDY

24 LAUNDRY

25 KITCHEN

26 JUNIOR COMMON ROOM

27 ART MUSEUM

28 SENIOR LABORATORY

29 SENIOR WORKSHOP

30 REFERENCE AND NON-FICTION LIBRARY

31 JUNIOR WORKSHOP

32 MASTERS' COMMON ROOM

33 PHOTOGRAPHY DARK ROOM

34 MUSIC ROOM

35 JUNIOR LABORATORY

36 JUNIOR ART STUDIO

37 RECEPTION ROOM

38 REHEARSAL ROOM

39 ENGINEER'S ROOM*

40 LIBRARIAN'S ROOM

41 FICTION LIBRARY

42 THE RAG

43 LOUNGE: WRITING ROOM

44 CLOAKS: TOILETS

---

* Boiler room and fuel stores are located in basement.

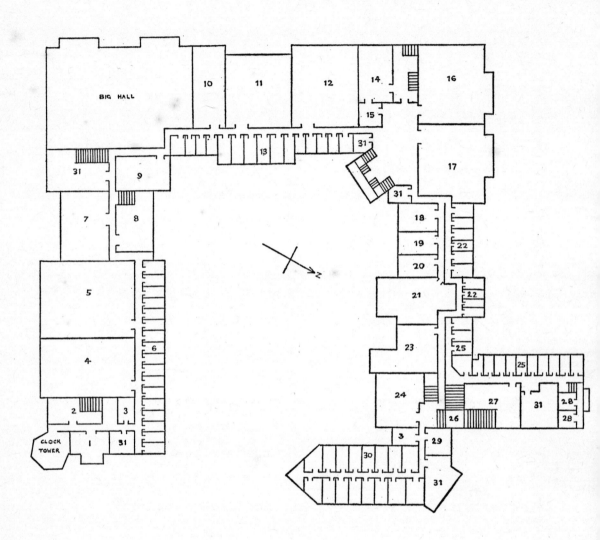

Greyfriars School

FIRST FLOOR PLAN

1 UPPER FOURTH FORM CLUB ROOM

2 LOUNGE: WRITING ROOM

3 BOX ROOM

4 UPPER FOURTH FORM CLASS ROOM

5 REMOVE FORM CLASS ROOM

6 UPPER FOURTH FORM STUDIES

7 SIXTH FORM CLASS ROOM

8 SPORTS MEETING ROOM

9 SIXTH FORM CLUB ROOM

10 DANCING TUITION ROOM

11 FIFTH FORM CLASS ROOM

12 SHELL FORM CLASS ROOM

13 SIXTH FORM STUDIES

14 SERVANTS' HALL

15 BOOT AND SHOE ROOM

16 SECOND FORM CLASS ROOM

17 THIRD FORM CLASS ROOM

18 THIRD FORM CLUB ROOM

19 SECOND FORM CLUB ROOM

20 FAGS' ROOM

21 FIRST FORM CLASS ROOM

22 SHELL FORM STUDIES

23 SHELL FORM CLUB ROOM

24 FIFTH FORM CLUB ROOM

25 REMOVE FORM STUDIES

26 REMOVE STAIRCASE AND LANDING

27 REMOVE FORM CLUB ROOM

28 REMOVE BOX ROOMS

29 FIFTH FORM GAMES STUDY

30 FIFTH FORM STUDIES

31 BATHS: TOILETS

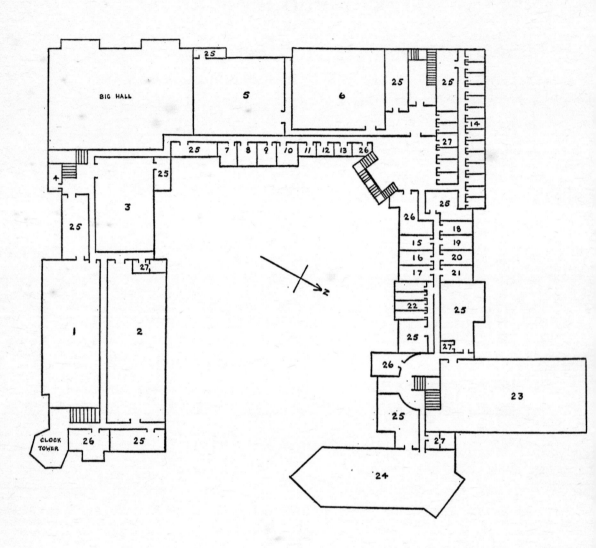

Greyfriars School
SECOND FLOOR PLAN

1 SHELL FORM DORMITORY

2 UPPER FOURTH FORM DORMITORY

3 THIRD FORM DORMITORY

4 PUNISHMENT ROOM

5 FIRST FORM DORMITORY

6 SECOND FORM DORMITORY

7 MR HACKER'S BEDROOM

8 MR PROUT'S BEDROOM

9 MR CAPPER'S BEDROOM

10 MR QUELCH'S BEDROOM

11 MR B. M. TWIGG'S BEDROOM

12 MR WIGGINS'S BEDROOM

13 MR E. TWIGG'S BEDROOM

14 SIXTH FORM BEDROOMS

15 MR LASCELLES'S BEDROOM

16 M. CHARPENTIER'S BEDROOM

17 HERR OTTO GANS'S BEDROOM

18 MATRON'S ROOM

19 COOKS' ROOM

20, 21 HOUSEMAIDS' ROOMS

22 GUEST ROOMS

23 REMOVE FORM DORMITORY

24 FIFTH FORM DORMITORY

25 BATHS: TOILETS

26 LOUNGE: WRITING ROOM

27 LINEN STORES: BOX ROOMS: SPARE ROOMS

Some Members of the Teaching Staff

DR LOCKE

The Headmaster. Liked by all. A sincere, kind and just man—ideal qualities for a Headmaster.

It is thought that when Dr Locke retires he will recommend as his successor Mr Quelch—the efficient and capable Remove master.

MR PROUT

The portly master of the Fifth; is widely travelled and noted for long-winded stories of his hunting exploits of days gone by, when he visited the "Rockies".

Justifies the nickname of "Old Pompous", but is good-natured and on the whole well liked by his form.

MR HACKER

Master of the Shell. Has a rather acid demeanour; maintains strict discipline in his form.

MR QUELCH

Remove master; is strict and stern (his "gimlet eyes" are the terror of slackers and wrongdoers), but very fair and is respected. He enjoys long country walks and a game of chess with his favourite opponent, Mr Lambe the vicar. But his greatest interest is the compilation of his famous *A History of Greyfriars*.

Sometimes referred to by his form as "Henry" (but not in his hearing).

MR LASCELLES

Mathematics and Games master. Is well liked and probably the most popular master in the School. Nicknamed "Larry" by the Juniors.

M. CHARPENTIER

A likeable man, but inclined to be too easy-going; accordingly he becomes the victim of leg-pulling in the form room, when he takes French or holds detention.

Some Scholars

SIXTH FORM

Wingate, George Bernard (School Captain, Head Prefect, Head of Games)

Benson, Howard	Loder, Gerald Assheton
Carne, Arthur Woodhead	North, Tom
Coker, Reginald (Minor)	Reynolds, Robert Malcolm
Doone, Arthur (Major)	Tremaine, Charles
Faulkner, Lawrence	Walker, James
Gwynne, Patrick	Yates, George Frederick
Hammersley, Vincent	

WINGATE, GEORGE BERNARD

Captain of Greyfriars; Head Prefect; Head of Games. The most popular fellow at Greyfriars. A great skipper and a splendid all-round sportsman. Maintains discipline, whilst encouraging good feeling throughout the School. Has a younger brother in the Third form. His home is in Chester.

BENSON, HOWARD

A studious fellow, a chum of Coker Minor.

CARNE, ARTHUR WOODHEAD

A friend of Loder; inclined to bully. Plays in the Senior XIs, but spoils his chances of achievement by trying to act the "gay dog".

COKER, REGINALD (MINOR)

The weakly brother of the great Horace. A good scholar (he is younger than his brother who is still in the Fifth form) but a hopeless disciplinarian. Often ill-treated by bullies but stoutly championed by his brother. Lives with his family in his Aunt Judy's house—Coker Place—in Surrey.

DOONE, ARTHUR (MAJOR)

A big, burly senior, who backs Wingate to the hilt and can put up a strong scrap if necessary. Has a brother in the Upper Fourth.

FAULKNER, LAWRENCE

A prefect and chum of Wingate. Upholds discipline and has all-round ability. A very keen footballer. A close friend of Tremaine and like him a West Countryman.

GWYNNE, PATRICK

Irish and a jolly good sort. Wingate's closest friend. Sunny-tempered and easy-going, he is liked by everyone and is especially popular with the fags.

Excels on the sports field, and has made the highest individual score in Greyfriars cricket history—226 not out against Friardale Village—since Clifton's famous 244 against the same club in 1899.

HAMMERSLEY, VINCENT
A tall, strapping prefect and an all-round sportsman.

LODER, GERALD ASSHETON
Known as the "black sheep" of the School. Uses his position of prefect to indulge in bullying. Often falls foul of the Removites.

NORTH, TOM
An easy-going prefect, who usually looks after the fags. Is greatly liked by them because of his good nature.

REYNOLDS, ROBERT MALCOLM
A good fellow, who makes a good leader if under pressure but never pushes himself forward in any way.

TREMAINE, CHARLES
One of the tallest of the Sixth form. A good average Senior and prefect. Both he and his chum Faulkner hail from the West of England.

WALKER, JAMES
A prefect who, from time to time, has associated with Loder and Carne. Fortunately he tends now to take more interest in School games and other activities and has shown a much better side of his nature.

YATES, GEORGE FREDERICK
A staunch Senior, participating in all Sixth Form enterprises.

FIFTH FORM

Blundell, George (Form Captain)

(Study No. 1)

	Study		Study
Bland, Bertram	1	Price, Stephen	5
Coker, Horace James (Major)	4	Smith, Edward William (Major)	2
Fitzgerald, Terrence	2	Tomlinson, Thomas Trotter	
Greene, William Frederick	4	(Major)	6
Hilton, Cedric	6	Wavery, Frank	3
Potter, George	4		

BLUNDELL, GEORGE

> Captain of the Fifth. An energetic fellow of sound principles. A valuable man in the Senior football and cricket XIs. On the whole has loyal support from the form, and always the support of his great friend, Bland.

BLAND, BERTRAM

> Has been Blundell's closest friend since their days together in the Third and supports him staunchly. A good sportsman and a fellow much on Blundell's pattern.

COKER, HORACE JAMES (MAJOR)

> The biggest and burliest member of the Fifth. Has a great opinion of his abilities in class and on the sports field; but is the despair of his formmaster, Mr Prout, particularly with spelling, and causes great hilarity when in action at games. Has owned several motor-cycles and caused much damage to property by his erratic riding. Is doted on by his Aunt Judy, who supplies liberal quantities of cash and hampers. Likes to boss his study-mates Potter and Greene and adopts a condescending attitude towards all juniors, whom he refers to collectively as "fags". He is, however, honest and straightforward and very generous. Known to most as the "funny man" of the Fifth, which he cannot understand. Lives with his people in Coker Place, a house in Surrey owned by the wealthy Aunt Judy.

FITZGERALD, TERRENCE

> A cheery, good fellow, capable and humorous. Likes to poke fun at Horace Coker and in fact at life in general.

GREENE, WILLIAM FREDERICK

> One of Coker's two special chums. Appears to suffer Coker's awkward

ways because of the ample funds and supplies of tuck that Coker brings to their study. A bit of a poet, good at games and at heart quite a decent fellow.

HILTON, CEDRIC

A wealthy and elegant member of the form who hails from Devon. He is one of the Hiltons of Hilton Hall. Likes to indulge in the gay life and is a racing enthusiast. Has his moments of being a reasonable sort of fellow.

POTTER, GEORGE

The second study-mate of Horace Coker. He follows more or less the same pattern as Greene in his attitude towards the "funny man" of the Fifth. Is a useful member of the Senior football and cricket XIs.

PRICE, STEPHEN

A fellow of somewhat uncertain temperament. Dislikes sports. Has been known to associate with the racing fraternity at local hostelries. Was once friendly with Bulstrode of the Remove but this ended when Price moved from the Shell to the Fifth Form.

SMITH, EDWARD WILLIAM (MAJOR)

One of the right type. Has one brother in the Remove and another in the Second Form.

TOMLINSON, THOMAS TROTTER (MAJOR)

A burly fellow, very fond of boxing. Has a brother in the Upper Fourth.

WAVERY, FRANK

Always elegant, stylishly dressed and well supplied with money.

THE SHELL

Hobson, James (Form Captain)

(Study No. 5)

	Study		Study
Carr, Albert	1	Lange, Arnold Lawrence	6
Chowne, Cholmondeley	2	Miles, Samuel	1
Churchill, Luke	2	Rayner, Neil	3
Hoskins, Claude	5	Robinson, Jack	4
Jackson, Philbert	4	Stewart, Edward	3

HOBSON, JAMES
Captain of the form. Sturdy, muscular and a sound fellow. A good man at football and a keen cricketer.

CARR, ALBERT
A study-mate and chum of Miles and a member of the Middle School football XI.

CHOWNE, CHOLMONDELEY
A dandified fellow who is always seeking the society of the Sixth.

CHURCHILL, LUKE
Shares No. 2 study with Chowne. The pair seem to hit it off together, but Churchill is not an easy fellow to understand and, because of that, perhaps not very popular.

HOSKINS, CLAUDE
According to his own estimation, Claude Hoskins is the musical genius of Greyfriars. His study-mate Hobson is not in favour of Hoskins's "music" and his form-mates refer to his performances on the piano as a "thumping" nuisance. Has tried composing, without success.

JACKSON, PHILBERT
One of the "nuts". He does however, excel at ice-skating and is a very good roller-skater.

LANGE, ARNOLD LAWRENCE
Known generally as the "mad inventor"; unfortunately his inventions never work. When not involved with his weird ideas, has similar tastes to Jackson.

MILES, SAMUEL
Shares No. 1 study with Carr and, like him, plays for the Middle School football XI.

RAYNER, NEIL
   Study-mate of Stewart. A sound fellow who is interested in writing.

ROBINSON, JACK
   Shares a study with Jackson and is a fellow of his type. Is particularly
   bright in class and often lends a hand to Jackson, who is not too good at
   form work.

STEWART, EDWARD
   A firm, resolute Scot, and a good sort.

UPPER FOURTH

Temple, Cecil Reginald (Form Captain)
(Study No. 2)

	Study		Study
Angel, Aubrey	6	Murphy, Shamus	1
Dabney, William Walter	2	Phipps, Charles	8
Doone, Percy (Minor)	7	Scott, James Kenneth	5
Fitzgerald, Patrick	4	Tomlinson, Teddy Edwin	
Fry, Edward	2	(Minor)	5
Kennedy, Paul	6	Turner, Maurice	3
MacDougall, Ronald	4		

TEMPLE, CECIL REGINALD

He is Captain of the form. Son of the wealthy Sir Reginald Temple. An elegantly dressed fellow whose family live in an elegant house in London's Grosvenor Square. He is recognised as one of the "nuts". Conceited—especially as to his own abilities. This idea is fostered by his two friends Dabney and Fry. Often feuds with the Remove, invariably coming off second best.

ANGEL, AUBREY

A dandy, who tends to be unscrupulous in his general attitudes. Had an unfortunate early life—spent largely among the society of gaming saloons. Angel was known to Temple, Vernon-Smith and Jimmy Vivian before he came to Greyfriars. He owns a powerful motor-cycle which causes some havoc each term.

DABNEY, WILLIAM WALTER

One of Temple's two close friends. Possesses much more common sense than his chief, but has yet to show sufficient initiative to restrain any of Temple's conceited actions. A good athlete, although athletics is a branch of sport for which Temple has little consideration. Dabney's time-worn rejoinder of "Oh, rather!" expresses his opinion of most remarks addressed to him.

DOONE, PERCY (MINOR)

Has a brother in the Sixth. A fellow always willing to back up Scott rather than Temple. Suggests many wheezes against the Remove and takes full credit for any that are used.

FITZGERALD, PATRICK

A cousin of Fitzgerald of the Fifth. Very much like him in ways—about twice as "mad"—and talks with a pronounced Irish accent.

FRY, EDWARD
   Temple's other chum. Inclined to be a dandy but is generally a stronger character than the Form Captain or Dabney, and plays in the Middle School football XI. Seems content to take a follow-my-leader role.

KENNEDY, PAUL
   The study-mate of Aubrey Angel. Is little more than a toady and hanger-on to Angel.

MacDOUGALL, RONALD
   A lad from the Highlands. Sporty, but quick tempered.

MURPHY, SHAMUS
   A wild Irishman from Connemara. Interested in photography and sometimes writes poetry. True to his friends and a decent fellow in his own peculiar way.

PHIPPS, CHARLES
   A satellite of Temple. Has plenty of cash and is something of a dandy—but little else.

SCOTT, JAMES KENNETH
   The most level-headed fellow in the Fourth. He resembles Johnny Bull of the Remove in some ways—especially when he stonewalls in cricket.

TOMLINSON, TEDDY EDWIN (MINOR)
   Has a brother in the Fifth. Very friendly with his study-mate Scott. Both derive amusement from Temple's stupidity. Tomlinson is robust perhaps even on the portly side.

TURNER, MAURICE
   An average form member. Quite a good actor and a prominent member of the Upper Fourth Dramatic Society.

LOWER FOURTH
(THE REMOVE)

Wharton, Harry (Form Captain)

(Study No. 1)

	Study		Study
Bolsover, Percy (Major)	10	Nugent, Frank (Major)	1
Brown, Tom	2	Ogilvy, Donald Robert	3
Bull, John	14	Penfold, Richard	9
Bulstrode, George	2	Rake, Richard	6
Bunter, William George (Major)	7	Redwing, Tom	4
Cherry, Robert	13	Russell, Richard	3
Delarey, Piet	12	Singh, Hurree Jamset Ram	
Desmond, Michael	6	(H.R.H. the Nabob of Bhani-	
Dupont, Napoleon	10	pur)	13
Dutton, Tom	7	Skinner, Harold	11
Field, Sampson Quincy Iffley	14	Smith, Robert Fortescue (Minor)	8
Fish, Fisher Tarleton	14	Snoop, Sidney James	11
Hazeldene, Peter	2	Stott, William	11
Hillary, Richard	5	Todd, Peter Hastings	7
Kipps, Oliver	5	Treluce, Anthony	9
Linley, Mark	13	Trevor, Herbert Beauchamp	9
Mauleverer, The Rt. Hon. the		Vernon-Smith, Herbert Tudor	4
Earl of	12	Vivian, Sir James (Bart)	12
Morgan, David	6	Wibley, William Ernest	6
Newland, Montague	9	Wun Lung	13

WHARTON, HARRY

Captain of the Remove. An orphan, he lives in Surrey with his guardian Colonel James Wharton of Wharton Lodge. As a new boy he was head-strong and perverse, but soon changed in his ways and carved out a niche for himself at Greyfriars, replacing Bulstrode as Form Captain. He skippers the Middle School football and cricket XIs and takes a prominent part in all Remove activities. Wharton is a born leader, brave, a staunch friend. Although not a brilliant scholar he is hard-working and conscientious. Takes his Captain's duties seriously, upholds discipline and in general is a credit to the School. He is the acknowledged leader of the "Famous Five".

STUDIES AND THEIR OCCUPANTS

LOWER FOURTH (THE REMOVE) GREYFRIARS SCHOOL

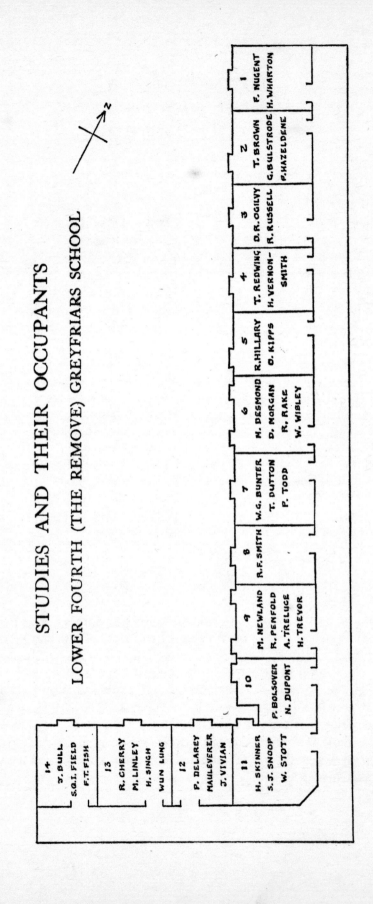

N

1 — F. NUGENT, H. WHARTON

2 — T. BROWN, G. BULSTRODE, P. HAZELDENE

3 — D. R. OGILVY, R. RUSSELL

4 — T. REDWING, H. VERNON-SMITH

5 — R. HILLARY, O. KIPPS

6 — H. DESMOND, D. MORGAN, R. RAKE, W. WIBLEY

7 — W. G. BUNTER, T. DUTTON, P. TODD

8 — R. F. SMITH

9 — M. NEWLAND, R. PENFOLD, A. TRELUCE, H. TREVOR

10 — P. BOLSOVER, N. DUPONT

11 — H. SKINNER, S. J. SNOOP, W. STOTT

12 — P. DELAREY, MAULEVERER, J. VIVIAN

13 — R. CHERRY, M. LINLEY, H. SINGH, WUN LUNG

14 — J. BULL, S.Q.I. FIELD, F.T. FISH

BOLSOVER, PERCY (MAJOR)

Big and burly and at one time an inveterate bully, but this failing has been curtailed to a large extent after pressure from other Remove "strong men". Has a somewhat surly manner but on the whole is not a bad fellow and appears to get on very well with his study-mate Dupont. Has a brother in the Third.

BROWN, TOM

A New Zealand boy from North Island's Taraneki. His father is a director of a New Zealand air line. A popular, reliable fellow, always cheery and a good all-round sportsman. Interested in music. Celebrated his arrival at Greyfriars by kicking a football all the way from Friardale station to the School.

BULL, JOHN

Known to his friends as Johnny. The last member to join and thus form the "Famous Five". A sturdy young Yorkshireman from Moor Fell in the West Riding who speaks—and hits—straight from the shoulder when roused. Once he forms an opinion it is almost impossible to get him to change. Johnny is invaluable in a scrap and is a generous and loyal friend. A good sportsman, noteworthy as a stonewaller in cricket. Likes to play the concertina, although his form-mates have mixed feelings about the sounds he produces.

BULSTRODE, GEORGE

Was at one time Captain of the Remove, until supplanted by Wharton. In those days he was not a very pleasant fellow and indulged in bullying. His nature changed when his younger brother, Herbert, died. Bulstrode, although not now in the limelight, has remained a useful man at games and is a fine goalkeeper.

BUNTER, WILLIAM GEORGE

The most famous personality of Greyfriars School is also the fattest and unwittingly the funniest member of the Remove. Is extremely short-sighted without his "big, round spectacles" which, with his rolling gait, have earned for him the nickname of the "Owl". Earns himself endless bootings and cuffs as a result of his habits of helping himself to other people's tuck, listening at keyholes and telling "whoppers". Bunter has no equal in the rapid disposal of vast quantities of tuck. His attempts to borrow money against a long-delayed postal order from rich or titled relations have become legendary in the Remove. Has weird notions of right and wrong, truth and fiction—apparently thinking there is very little difference. Bunter's performances in class, particularly with Latin and spelling, produce great amusement for the form in general, but exasperate Mr Quelch to the limit. Bunter is an excellent man at sleeping and general laziness—taking great pains to dodge games practice and all other forms of exertion. He has one gift at which he is an accepted expert —ventriloquism—and has often used this to further some intricate schemes, occasionally with unfortunate results for himself. As holiday times approach, Bunter makes concentrated efforts to get invitations and, by various tortuous methods, has often succeeded, thereby becoming involved in adventures in many parts of the world—the Middle and Far East, the Continent, America and the South Seas. He is fond of breaking rules but is indignant when punished and complains bitterly of continued injustice from everyone in authority. His invariable opening remark in any conversation is—"I say, you fellows". The best-known member of a well-known and large Surrey family (all its members have a striking resemblance to each other), Bunter has a brother in the Second form, a sister Bessie at Cliff House School and a cousin Walter who was for a short time form-master of the First form at Greyfriars. His father, Mr Samuel Bunter, is a stockbroker, who often expresses annoyance at his son's shortcomings, both in the scholastic and sports fields. *Home address:* Bunter Villa, Reigate, Surrey.

CHERRY, ROBERT

The third member of the "Famous Five", Bob Cherry is without doubt the best-liked fellow in the Remove. He has a wonderful cheerfulness and an almost perpetual smile in face of all upsets. He is generous, a champion of the under-dogs and shows tolerance to all—even such exasperating people as Bunter and Skinner. Bob is a first-class sportsman and recognised as the handiest fellow with his fists in the form. Usually takes upon himself the early morning task of rousing Bunter and Mauleverer from their slumbers. His cheery greeting—"Hallo, hallo, hallo"—has become part of everyday Remove life. His father is Major Cherry, a gallant and now retired Army officer, who lives in Cherry Place, the family house in Dorset.

DELAREY, PIET

The boy from South Africa. Has been nicknamed "the rebel" because of his fiery spirit, which has led him to cheek those in authority when occasion seemed to warrant. On the whole is a decent fellow and has been a good friend to Jimmy Vivian.

DESMOND, MICHAEL

Known as Micky or "young Tipperary". Real Irish with a brogue to match, and the amusement this gives to his form-mates is taken in good part by Desmond. Good-natured, but has sometimes been persuaded to play the goat, although not to any great length. He is friendly with David Morgan.

DUPONT, NAPOLEON

Comes from France. Shares a study with Bolsover and had many arguments with him at first, but has now settled down. One of the lesser lights, but a decent fellow. Noted mainly for the mysterious dishes he likes to cook and which he tries to persuade all and sundry to sample.

DUTTON, TOM

Has the unfortunate handicap of poor hearing. He is a good skater, both roller and ice, and would be a useful sportsman were it not for his deafness. Has a high regard for Peter Todd and the opposite for Bunter. Enjoys reading as a pastime.

FIELD, SAMPSON QUINCY IFFLEY

Hails from New South Wales. A good fellow in every way and an excellent batsman. Known universally as "Squiff"—a name bestowed upon him by Bob Cherry, who saw the initials "S.Q.I.F." on the new arrival's luggage. Is noted for his great wheezes and introduced himself to Greyfriars by playing a grand jape on Ponsonby & Co. of Highcliffe.

FISH, FISHER TARLETON

The guy from a penthouse aptly named "The Aquariam" in "Noo" York in the "Yewnited" States. His world revolves almost exclusively around money and the amassing of the same. Is called "Fishy" by the Removites, who hold the opinion that his money-making schemes match his nickname. He is tolerated by study-mates Bull and Field, but is frequently lectured by them on his peculiar idea of honesty in business dealings.

HAZELDENE, PETER

Has improved since the early days when the Remove called him "Vaseline". But he is still weak-willed and inclined to passionate outbursts. At times indulges in his old failing of gambling, which has led him into some dangerous situations. When in the mood, can be a useful man at games. Has a sister—Marjorie—at Cliff House School who is his extreme opposite and a great favourite with the Remove fellows.

HILLARY, RICHARD

When he first came to Greyfriars his conscience would not allow him to raise his fists to anyone—even a bold Bunter was able to challenge him with impunity. Circumstances then changed and Hillary discovered he was useful in a scrap. Is now quite happy with his study companion Kipps.

KIPPS, OLIVER

Not in the forefront of form affairs, but can claim distinction as a conjuror of great ability and has amazed his schoolfellows at times with his skill. Not bad at sports—he is an excellent all-round gymnast—but in games as well as his studies he has limited staying powers.

LINLEY, MARK

The scholarship boy from Bury, Lancashire. Had to fight the persecution of snobs during his early days at Greyfriars. Fortunately he had the support of Bob Cherry during these difficult times and now Bob is probably his best friend. He is without doubt the most brilliant scholar in the Remove. A fellow of the best type; a first-class sportsman with a place in the School XIs.

MAULEVERER, THE RT. HON. THE EARL OF. HERBERT PLANTAGENET
    MAULEVERER

The Rt. Hon. the Earl of Mauleverer, of Mauleverer Towers in Hampshire. Lord Mauleverer is a millionaire—under the guardianship of his uncle, Sir Reginald Brooke. Has been nicknamed "Mauly" for short. He is invariably placid and languid and takes every opportunity to relax. When occasion demands, however, he has a great deal of pluck and gives a good account of himself in a tight corner. Has wisdom and clear thinking, often acting as peacemaker in heated disagreements. His tastefully furnished study is shared by Delarey and Vivian, with whom he is on quite friendly terms.

MORGAN, DAVID

A Welsh boy and good fellow in general. Has sometimes been tempted to the wrong track, although this does not last. Has a quick temper but no malice. Comes from Caernarvon, in North Wales.

NEWLAND, MONTAGUE

A Jewish boy from Hove in Sussex who is justly popular in the Remove. Is wise and generous in his ways and has lots of pluck. Thinks a great deal of his Uncle Isaac, who is his guardian and keeps Newland well supplied with cash.

NUGENT, FRANK (MAJOR)

Was the first of the "Famous Five" to arrive at Greyfriars. He is Wharton's closest friend and loyal companion. Very good-looking, he has sometimes been called effeminate by those who know him least. Nugent, however, quickly kills that idea by his prowess on the sports field and handiness with the gloves. Has been caused worry by his younger brother in the Second, who has sometimes been involved in awkward escapades. His family live near Amesbury, in Wiltshire.

OGILVY, DONALD ROBERT

A sturdy Scot from Inverness. Resolute and capable; reliable in every respect. Closely attached to his chum, Russell, who shares a study with him. Has a keen ambition to become an architect one day.

PENFOLD, RICHARD

A scholarship boy, the son of a Friardale cobbler. Like Linley, had a tough time when first at Greyfriars, from the snobbish element; but he conquered this antagonism by his grit and determination. Is famous for his verse, which he often composes. A very good scholar and in the fore-front as an all-rounder in sports, where he has made a name for himself as a distance runner.

RAKE, RICHARD

Known always as Dick. A cheerful personality with a great deal of pluck and resolution. Is a loyal friend when trouble arises.

REDWING, TOM

One of the most reliable and good-natured fellows in the Remove. Was originally a scholarship boy from near-by Hawkscliff but became in-dependent when bequeathed a large sum of money by his uncle. First came to the School under the name "Leonard Clavering" and had a very miserable time. Twice he left Greyfriars but returned the second time to stay, through the efforts of Vernon-Smith. After moving from Snoop's study to share No. 4 with the "Bounder", he settled down. A bond of friendship has developed between the two and Redwing has proved him-self a loyal chum ever since. He is one of the few people from whom Vernon-Smith will take advice. He is a clever scholar and a very good man at sports.

RUSSELL, RICHARD

A good, steady type. Has developed skill as a boxer and participated in several schoolboy championship fights. Is the bosom pal of Ogilvy and has found this boy's support of value during certain periods when he seemed to be going off the rails.

SINGH, HURREE JAMSET RAM. H.R.H. THE NABOB OF BHANIPUR

His Royal Highness is well liked generally and a valued member of the "Famous Five". Known to all as "Inky" on account of his dusky complexion. Came to Greyfriars to continue an education begun by his tutors at the Bhanipur Palace in India. Uses a wonderful and amusing variety of the English language and is particularly funny with his very mixed-up proverbs. He is a first-class sportsman, being noted for his deadly bowling on the cricket field.

SKINNER, HAROLD

Notorious as the cad of the Remove. Shares a study with Snoop and Stott, prior to which he was in Vernon-Smith's room. Skinner has a stronger character and is more cunning than his study-mates. He is spiteful; strives always to take revenge for any slight—real or imagined. Every decent fellow in the form dislikes him. He indulges in all the pursuits of the typical gay dog and has been known to crib in lessons. In earlier days Skinner almost succeeded in keeping Redwing from Greyfriars and was foiled only by Vernon-Smith's intervention.

SMITH, ROBERT FORTESCUE (MINOR)

Has two brothers at Greyfriars—in the Fifth and Second. Is the lone occupant of No. 8 study at present and does not often appear in the lime-light. An average Removite.

SNOOP, SIDNEY JAMES

He was a similar type to Skinner, but since those days has, to some extent, realised his follies. Still associates with Skinner, but it is hoped he will further improve his ways.

STOTT, WILLIAM

Skinner's other study-mate. He is content to tread in that fellow's foot-steps and to ape his questionable habits.

TODD, PETER HASTINGS

The leader of No. 7 study, who experiences difficulties with its other occupants—Bunter and Dutton. Is continually trying to make Bunter see the error of his ways, without effect. Todd's father is the well-known London solicitor with a house in Bloomsbury and Peter inherits his wisdom and shrewdness. A very nice fellow; popular; keen at sports. Does well in class.

TRELUCE, ANTHONY

Keeps himself very much in the background and appears quite content with this role. Has occasionally dabbled in gay dog habits, but to no great extent.

TREVOR, HERBERT BEAUCHAMP

A similar fellow to Treluce but more decisive. Son of a Lancashire manu-facturer and well supplied with cash. In the early days he played in the Junior XI with Morgan and Skinner, but as better players arrived they were replaced. Trevor is friendly with Treluce but does not mix very much with his other study-mates—Newland and Penfold.

VIVIAN, SIR JAMES (BART.)

Is related to Lord Mauleverer. As a youngster he lived in the slums of Carker's Rents, near the Euston Road. Rescued from there by Sir Reginald Brooke, Lord Mauleverer's uncle and guardian, and sent to Greyfriars. Has very little money. His early upbringing is reflected still in his poor manners and difficulty with aspirates. Is quick and alert.

VERNON-SMITH, HERBERT TUDOR

When he first came to Greyfriars, he well deserved the name of "Bounder" which was bestowed upon him. Is now generally referred to as "Smithy". Probably has the most controversial character in the School. Is the son of Samuel Vernon-Smith, the millionaire, and has an abundance of money. His people have a house in Courtman Square, London, and also own Seahill Park, in Sussex. He can be arrogant; hard as nails; has an unpredictable temper; and is extremely reckless. Goes through periods of smoking and gambling; not so much perhaps for honest enjoyment, but simply because they are against the rules. Is as honest and straightforward as the best with his form-mates, but would not hesitate to stray from the strict truth when dealing with persons of authority, should it suit his purpose. Is generous when in the mood. In times of danger keeps cool and sardonic and his fearless spirit is to be admired. Despite excursions into the gay life, Vernon-Smith is a first-class man at sports and very useful with his fists. When he decides to make the effort, can be in the forefront in class. The calm influence of his great pal Redwing has helped restrain some of his more wayward recklessness. Vernon-Smith is a fellow always prominent in one way or another.

WIBLEY, WILLIAM ERNEST

His great claim to fame is as an actor of unusual ability. Noted for his clever impersonations, is fond of suggesting japes wherein he can demonstrate his genius. In the main he is a decent, steady fellow. General Manager of the Remove's Dramatic Society.

WUN LUNG

The Chinese junior. Is a likeable chap, despite a few faults. He is crafty and has some difficulty in sticking to the truth. Finds it useful not to "savvy" in any awkward situation. As a new boy at Greyfriars he was persecuted by Bulstrode. Devoted to his young brother Hop Hi of the Second Form and thinks highly of Bob Cherry. A very good gymnast and table tennis player.

PERSONAL DETAILS OF THE LOWER FOURTH FORM

(The Remove)

	AGE		HEIGHT		WEIGHT	
	yr.	mth.	ft.	in.	st.	lb.
Wharton, H. (Form Captain)	15	4	5	5	7	12
Bolsover, P. (Major)	16	2	5	$5\frac{1}{2}$	9	4
Brown, T.	15	2	5	$3\frac{1}{2}$	7	9
Bull, J	15	3	5	2	9	4
Bulstrode, G	15	9	5	4	8	1
Bunter, W. G. (Major)	15	1	4	9	14	$12\frac{1}{2}$
Cherry, R.	15	2	5	$4\frac{1}{2}$	8	3
Delarey, P.	14	10	5	3	7	10
Desmond, M.	14	11	5	0	7	5
Dupont, N.	15	0	4	11	7	0
Dutton, T.	15	4	5	2	8	1
Field, S. Q. I.	15	3	5	4	8	0
Fish, F. T.	15	4	5	1	7	4
Hazeldene, P.	15	1	5	$1\frac{1}{2}$	7	3
Hillary, R.	15	4	5	3	8	1
Kipps, O.	14	11	5	0	7	2
Linley, M.	15	7	5	5	8	2
Mauleverer, Earl of	15	3	5	$1\frac{1}{2}$	6	12
Morgan, D.	14	10	4	11	6	13
Newland, M.	14	3	5	2	7	12
Nugent, F. (Major)	14	10	5	$2\frac{1}{2}$	7	7
Ogilvy, D. R.	15	0	5	5	7	12
Penfold, R.	15	1	5	3	8	0
Rake, R.	14	11	5	$4\frac{1}{2}$	7	8
Redwing, T.	15	8	5	5	8	12
Russell, R.	14	11	5	$4\frac{1}{2}$	7	10
Singh, H. J. R., H.R.H.	14	11	5	3	7	5
Skinner, H.	15	6	5	$4\frac{1}{2}$	7	3
Smith, R. F. (Minor)	14	8	5	$1\frac{1}{2}$	7	0
Snoop, S. J.	15	5	5	3	7	13
Stott, W.	15	7	5	$4\frac{1}{2}$	8	4
Todd, P. H.	15	10	5	$6\frac{1}{2}$	7	13
Treluce, A.	15	8	5	3	7	12
Trevor, H. B.	14	11	4	11	7	3
Vernon-Smith, H. T.	15	10	5	5	8	1
Vivian, Sir James	14	4	4	11	7	0
Wibley, W. E.	15	3	5	0	7	12
Wun Lung	14	3	4	$5\frac{1}{2}$	6	0

THIRD FORM

Bolsover, Hubert (Minor)
Bolter, Oliver
Conrad, Leonard
Lunn, Harold
O'Rourke, Tom

Paget, Percival Spencer
Simpson, John
Tubb, George
Wingate, Jack (Minor)

BOLSOVER, HUBERT
Quite a nice lad, although another with an unlucky early life in the slums, who had a lot to learn when sent to Greyfriars. He did not get much help from his elder brother in the Remove, who seemed to resent his coming. But despite this, he conquered his difficulties and is now well-liked in the form and is prominent among the fags.

BOLTER, OLIVER
Wields some influence in Lower School matters but is not very prominent, although fancying himself as one of the leaders.

CONRAD, LEONARD
A loyal henchman of Tubb.

LUNN, HAROLD
An average Third Former of no special distinction.

PAGET, PERCIVAL SPENCER
Tubb's right-hand man, although rather different in his ways—being something of a dandy. But is plucky enough.

SIMPSON, JOHN
A strange kid, with a very large pair of glasses. Becomes wildly excitable in his support of Tubb.

TUBB, GEORGE
The recognised leader of the Greyfriars fags and their forthright champion. A shock-headed youth who is given to grunting and grumbling. He is a good lad and a very useful bowler on the cricket field. He has, however, an exaggerated opinion of the fags' prowess at sports.

WINGATE, JACK (MINOR)
Brother of the School Captain, and like him comes from Chester. Has been spoiled and has big ideas of his own importance. Will probably be quite a decent, normal kid when he comes down to earth.

SECOND FORM

Bunter, Samuel Tuckless (Minor)
Castle, Thomas
Gatty, George Adalbert
Hop Hi
Marsden, Eric
Myers, Edwin
Nugent, Richard (Minor)

Pettifer, James
Smith, Harry (Junior)
Spring, Conrad Arthur
Sylvester, Roderick
Tatton, Rowland
Todd, Ernest

BUNTER, SAMUEL TUCKLESS

In appearance, a slightly smaller image of the famous "W.G." Resembles him also in his capacity for eating. He is not, however, quite such a spinner of yarns or "borrower" of other people's property. Appears to get on fairly well with his form-fellows. *Home address:* Bunter Villa, Reigate, Surrey.

GATTY, GEORGE ADALBERT

Another accepted leader of the fag brigade. A cheeky lad but cheerful and good natured.

HOP HI

Younger brother of Wun Lung of the Remove.

MYERS, EDWIN

A friend of Gatty and a similar type. Supports his pal loyally.

NUGENT, RICHARD (MINOR)

The younger brother of Frank. Got off to a bad start, having been spoiled at home. Caused his brother a lot of worry with his waywardness and defiance. Gradually became more sensible and developed into a reasonable lad. Has made local fame by his creation of "Dr Birchemall", whose antics are recounted in *The Greyfriars Herald.*

SYLVESTER, RODERICK E.

The son of an American multi-millionaire.

Principal Domestic Staff

MRS KEBBLE. *Matron and House Dame*

A kindly, motherly soul who, nevertheless, does not allow any nonsense.

Has the very responsible position of caring for the general welfare of the Greyfriars Scholars—a job which she handles with quiet efficiency.

A verse from one of the School songs sums it up neatly:

> *Of all the pebbles on the beach*
> *The most illustrious pebble*
> *That's ever come within our reach*
> *Is good old Mrs Kebble.*
> *This lady fairly fills the bill.*
> *She rules the downstairs regions;*
> *It is her daily task to fill*
> *The hungry schoolboy legions.*

WILLIAM GOSLING. *School Porter*

Reputed to be the oldest inhabitant of Greyfriars—both in years and service. Certain juniors have been heard to remark that "Gossy" (as he is nicknamed) has been there since the days of the Friars.

A crusty character, he is often the butt of junior leg-pulling, which probably encourages his opinion of schoolboys in general as "young rips". It is suspected, however, that Gosling would not want any other life and he is apparently happy in his own grumpy way.

His favourite opening phrase for any discussion—"Wot I says, is this 'ere"—has almost become part of School history. As a verse from one of the School songs says:

> *Then, when the weary day is O'er*
> *Within his lodge you'll find him;*
> *He loves to sit alone and snore,*
> *With cushions piled behind him.*
> *Rheumatics haunt him—it's a shame,*
> *And he is old and mossy;*
> *But Greyfriars wouldn't be the same*
> *Without our dear old Gossy.*

FRED TROTTER. *House Page Boy*

A lad with plenty of cheek; but a good, honest fellow and popular with most of the Scholars.

JOSEPH MIMBLE. *Head Gardener and Groundsman*

Husband of Mrs Jessie Mimble.

Mrs Jessie Mimble. *Keeper of the Tuck Shop*

A jolly, popular lady who, after years of experience in handling schoolboys, knows how to control the Greyfriars Scholars.

Has to be very firm on the question of supplies "on tick", particularly with fellows like Bunter.

Jones

Boat-keeper and son of Mr Jones, the proprietor of the well-known boat-building firm of the same name in Friardale.

Relatives of some Greyfriars Personalities

BUNTER, THE MISSES PRUDENCE AND REBECCA
Maiden aunts of the Bunter brothers. They are ladies of high principle, who believe in discipline and hard work, particularly where William George is concerned. Like Mr W. S. Bunter, they have strong views on financial support for their nephew.

BUNTER, WALTER
A cousin of the Bunter brothers who was once the form-master of the First form at Greyfriars. Similar in appearance to Bunter Major but, happily, not in habits.

BUNTER, WILLIAM SAMUEL
The father of William George and Samuel Tuckless Bunter. A stockbroker whose fortunes vary from time to time. Has several pet aversions—his eldest son's term reports, bad spelling, laziness and requests for money, American horror films, rising costs (especially school fees), figuring prominently among those which constantly strain relationships between father and son.

CARTER, UNCLE
An uncle of the Bunter brothers who keeps a boarding-house at Folkestone. Believes in keeping noses, particularly nephews' noses, to the grindstone.

CHERRY, SIR WILLIAM
Bob Cherry's uncle. He once rented a large house near Courtfield.

COKER, MISS JUDY
The aunt and benefactress of Horace (particularly) and Reginald Coker.

COOK, GEORGE
A cousin of the Bunter brothers who owns a holiday cruise yacht *Sea Nymph*.

LOCKE, FERRERS
Ferrers Locke, the famous private investigator, is a cousin of the Headmaster, Dr Locke. On several occasions he has been engaged to solve mysteries at the School.

OGILVY BROTHERS, THE
Donald Ogilvy of the Remove has six brothers, all of whom are in the Army.

REDWING, CAPTAIN JOHN
    Tom Redwing's father, a Captain in the Merchant Navy.

TODD, ALONZO
    A cousin of Peter Todd of the Remove, he was for a short time at Grey-
    friars, sharing No. 7 study with Todd, Dutton and Bunter.

WINGATE, BOB
    The elder brother of George and Jack Wingate, he is a Regular Army
    officer.

Places, People and General Information concerning the Environs of Greyfriars

Friardale

The old-world, picturesque village of Friardale is near to the School and popular with the boys. It has several fine specimens of well-preserved architecture, some of which date from the 16th century. Many of the inhabitants are well known and friendly to Greyfriars boys—encouraging a happy local atmosphere. A favourite meeting place of the scholars is the village bun shop, the proprietor of which is popularly known as "Uncle" Clegg—a kindly gentleman, liked by all.

The village cobbler is Mr Penfold, father of Dick Penfold, a Scholar of Greyfriars in the Remove, and his shop is consequently patronised by many of the Scholars.

Courtfield

A busy market town, which has a prominent place in the history of the area. It is the seat of the Rural District Council and contains the usual Administrative offices.

The town is well served by bus and train, and is within comfortable walking distance of Greyfriars—across Courtfield Common.

It offers entertainment in the form of a modern cinema and the Theatre Royal, which presents plays, concerts and, occasionally, ballet and opera.

Courtfield has a number of shops, the majority being old-established family concerns. There is, in addition, an up-to-date multiple store, Chunkley's, which deals in a wide selection of merchandise and can arrange almost any service. The store has also a first-class modern restaurant.*

Travel Facilities

RAIL: A branch line from the local station at Friardale connects with Courtfield Junction, and thence to Lantham, where a good service to neighbouring towns and to London is available.

BUS: The service which caters for travellers in the School vicinity, serves the towns of Courtfield, Redclyffe and Lantham. The route, within easy reach of Greyfriars School, is along the Courtfield–Lantham road.

TAXI: A reliable service is based at Courtfield Station. Taxis invariably meet all main line train arrivals.

---

* The restaurant and provisions departments of Chunkley's are rarely patronised by the average Greyfriars Scholar because of the high prices charged.

Table of Distances
Greyfriars to Friardale, just under 1 mile
       to Courtfield, about 3 miles
       to Hawkscliff, about 6 miles
       to Lantham, 10 miles
Courtfield to Pegg, 1 mile

Banks
There are branches of the Courtfield & County Bank, and the London &
Kentish Bank, in Courtfield and Friardale.

Newspapers
The local publications are:
    Friardale Gazette
    Courtfield & County Gazette
    Lantham Advertiser
    *Sporting Snips**

Hostelries
The best-known inns in the Greyfriars district are:
    The Three Fishers
    The Cross Keys
    The Bird in Hand

Popper Court
The home and estate of Sir Hilton Popper, Chairman of the Board of Governors of Greyfriars School, and one of the largest landowners.†

---

* This rather disreputable racing paper is banned at Greyfriars School.
† Sir Hilton does not take kindly to people wandering through his woods; everybody (including
the Greyfriars boys) is expected to keep strictly to the public footpath.

Local Nobilities and Personalities

Sir Julius Hogben—of Hogben Grange. A Governor of the School.

The Rev. Mr Lambe—Vicar of Friardale and School Chaplain.

Dr Pillbury—Friardale doctor and School Medical Officer.

Inspector Grimes—Officer-in-charge, Courtfield Police Station.

P.C. Tozer—Village Constable of Friardale.

Mr Boggs—Friardale Postman.

"Uncle" Clegg—Proprietor of Friardale bun shop.

Mr Cripps—Proprietor of the Carrier business, Courtfield.

Mr Joyce—Woodcutter, of Friardale.

Mr Jones—Friardale boat-builder (his nephew is boat-keeper at Greyfriars).

Mr Cobb—Landlord of The Cross Keys Inn.

Joe Banks, Bill Lodgey, "Soapy" Sanders, Jimmy Jugson—Members of the betting fraternity, bookmakers and their runners, who regrettably are usually to be contacted at the Three Fishers or the Cross Keys.

Neighbouring Schools

There are four large schools in the Greyfriars area—Highcliffe, Cliff House (Girls), Courtfield Grammar and Redclyffe.

The schools most closely associated with Greyfriars are Highcliffe and Cliff House. Some brief information regarding these is appended below.

HIGHCLIFFE

Headmaster—Dr Voysey
Fourth Form Master—Mr Mobbs
Prominent Fourth-formers: Frank Courtenay (Captain)
Rupert de Courcy (nicknamed "Caterpillar")

Gadsby
Monson
Cecil Ponsonby
Vavasour

(all known to the Greyfriars Scholars as "knuts and snobs")

Benson
Drury
Jones Minor
Merton
Smithson
Tunstall

School colours—Black and White

School Porter—Judson

CLIFF HOUSE

Headmistress—Miss Primrose
Fourth Form Mistress—Miss Bellew
Games Mistress—Miss Bullivant
Principal Fourth-formers: Barbara Redfern (Captain)
Bessie Bunter
Marjorie Hazeldene
Phyllis Howell
Dolly Joblin
Mabel Lynn
Clara Trevlyn (the tomboy)

Glossary of some Slang and Expressions
in use at Greyfriars

Bags	Trousers
Beak	Master
Black sheep	One who breaks accepted rules; a cad
Blub, blubbing	Cry, crying
Boater	Straw hat for summer wear
Bone	Take without permission
Book	An extra severe impot (q.v.)
Boot	Kick; e.g. to boot Bunter
Break bounds	Leave School premises during restricted hours or when forbidden to do so
Cackle	Laugh
Cheese it	Stop talking; Shut up
Chin-wag	Lengthy discussion
Chokey	Prison
Clobber	Clothing
Con	Construe, translate
Crib	Copy or cheat
Cuff	Slap, hit
Dic or Dick	Dictionary
Doorsteps and Dishwater	School tea in Hall
Dorm	Dormitory
Duck	In cricket, out for no score; nil
Dunning	Bookmaker's efforts to collect dues
Extra	Additional School work, out of class hours, as punishment
Fist	Handwriting
Fiver	Five-pound note
Footer	Football, Soccer
Funky	Scared
Gammon	Nonsense, rubbish
Gated	Kept within School precincts, as punishment

Gay dog	One who indulges in gambling, smoking, drinking, etc.
Grind	A long walk: also hard work
Hat trick	In football—three goals scored by one player
	In cricket—three wickets taken by one bowler
Hols	Holidays
Impot	Imposition—writing of lines as punishment
Jape	Practical joke
Jaw	Lecture, usually admonitory, also called pi-jaw
Jigger	Bicycle
Jip	Pain; annoyance
Lick	Chastise; beat somebody; win at games
Lip	Impertinence
Napper	Head
Nuts	Dandies
Oof	Money
Punny	Punishment Room
Pre	Prefect
Prep	Preparation—set work done during a certain part of the day in which essays, translations, etc., are written or prepared for the following day's lessons
Quack	Doctor
Quad	Quadrangle
Rag or jape	Practical joke
Rhino	Money
Right on the wicket	A pertinent statement
Roll	Roll call or calling-over
Sack or bunk	Expel from School
Sanny	Sanatorium
Scrap	Fight
Scrog	Food

Shipped	Upset and damaged—referring to contents of a room
Six on the bags	Six strokes of the cane
Smokes	Cigarettes
Spoof	To fool or deceive
Spread	A substantial meal; also to exaggerate
Stickers	Sweets, usually toffees
Stinks	Chemistry
Stuff	Spin a yarn; deceive
Tick	Pay later; promise to pay; on account
Tiffin	Lunch
Topper	Top hat
Trans	Translation
Tuck	Food; usually refers to cakes and confections
Up-end	Upset
Waxy	Bad tempered
Wheeze	An idea, a plan
Whopper	Untruth
Whops	Strokes with the cane
Yap	Irritating talk; nagging

Index

Quamdiu stabit Colosseus, stabit et Roma:
quando cadet Colosseus, cadet Roma:
quando cadet Roma, cadet et mundus.

The Venerable Bede

Quamdiu stabit Bunterus, stabit et Franciscus Ricardus:
quando cadet Bunterus, cadet Ricardus:
quando cadet Ricardus, cadet et ars scribendi juvenibus.

Frank Richards
In a B.B.C. broadcast, 19 September 1959

COMPILER'S ACKNOWLEDGEMENTS

I am well aware that in compiling and presenting this *Prospectus* I am making of myself a target for a booting by any number of people who, like myself, have been lifelong devotees of Greyfriars School. Some will declare that I have omitted certain details, ignored certain boys, misread certain characters, slandered certain masters or forgotten certain neighbours of the School. These criticisms I am ready to accept in part, saying only in my defence that often the source material was surprisingly incomplete for all its other riches, and sometimes directly contradictory of itself, in spite of the detailed factual records which Frank Richards kept of the legend he had created. In such cases I have had to weigh the evidence and present that version of a fact, or a name, or a detail, which seemed to me to fit best into the existing pattern. Or, more simply, when the balance seemed level I have chosen that version which appealed to me as an insatiable Greyfriars reader and note-maker. Other minor items I have omitted because I felt that they were irrelevant to the purpose or outside the scope of the *Prospectus* of a great public school. I have even, I confess, inserted in one short section material which my publisher calls "padding", to bridge a gap in the existing records. But I have used only *words* and not even under the provocation of thinking that "surely something must be here" have I inserted any *facts* in this "padding". The facts come only from the published stories of Greyfriars written over these many years by Frank Richards. Of these I would like to express my debt particularly to the *Greyfriars Holiday Annuals* of 1921, 1922, 1924, 1925, 1926 and 1927, which provided so many of the details of the School's history and life which could never have been gleaned from the stories. I am in debt of course to the old *Magnet* and other magazine sources of "Bunteriana", as I am to the thirty-eight books of the Greyfriars School series published by Cassell. My publisher, and Mrs Una Wright, the late Mr Richards' niece, have been very kind in letting me read and make notes from the typescripts of the last Frank Richards stories before they are published.

An earlier map of the Greyfriars district was printed in *The Magnet* of 2 March 1940, and was described by Mr Richards as "astonishingly like my own idea of the vicinity of the School". However, certain features shown there are at odds with details given in the published records, and I have therefore prepared my own maps. Although there is naturally an affinity between this earlier version and the maps printed here as endpapers and on pages 6 and 7, mine have the advantage that they could be checked against the publications of the last twenty-five years.

I must pay a debt of thanks to Mr Malcolm Arnold, who so happily provided a rousing new setting for one of the Greyfriars songs; and to

Mr D. P. Simpson of the classics department of that other great public school, Eton, who traced the source of the Greyfriars motto for me with a care which would have warmed the gimlet eyes of another well-known classicist. The assistance given me by the Royal College of Arms is acknowledged elsewhere: I would only add my thanks for the enthusiasm with which they undertook their task. Mr G. C. Foster not only shares my enthusiasm; he very kindly read my typescript and made some invaluable suggestions for improvement.

I have made my claims and my acknowledgements. I make now an apology. If any Greyfriars Scholar sees fit to disagree with what I have written, then I am sorry for his distress. But I am unrepentant for what I have done, and I trust that more will find pleasure in this book than will find fault. For whatever the reactions of the Greyfriars enthusiasts, this *Prospectus* was compiled as a labour of love solely for their delight, their interest, and their devotion to the traditions of the greatest school of all. And in that last sentiment I know we are all at one.

J. S. B.

January 1965

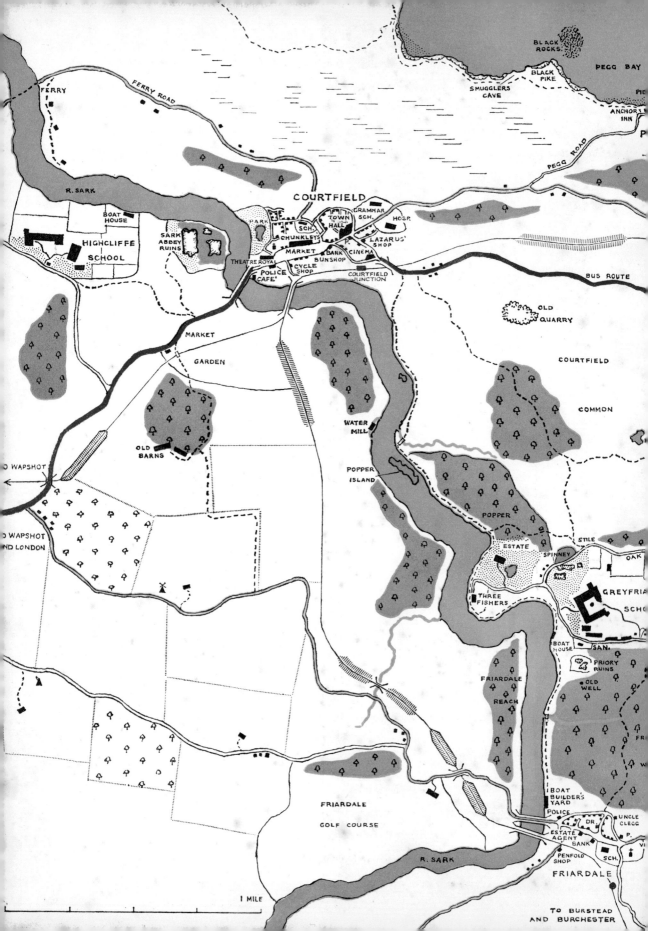